A Year Before
Christmas

by
Cathy Cade

FOR DIGGER

who wasn't afraid of Christmas Crackers

'Twas the night before Christmas
when Santa's new elf,
in the vast, silent workshop, sat all by herself.
She'd been fetching and carrying, sent to and fro
making tea, running errands – the least of the low.

And she'd mucked out the stables, not noticing that
daft old Rudolph was munching her new elven hat.
So it was, that when Santa Claus marshalled the rest
Emmie failed to pass muster – improperly dressed.

As the sleigh jingled off through the wintery skies,
Em recalled seeing oversized dark dragonflies
every day, as she shovelled snow, cold and downcast.
She'd heard them approach,
and she'd watched them drone past.

Metal mules don't need feeding or stalls mucking out.
She imagined a prototype – drafted it out.
And, because Emmie Elf was a born engineer,
it was ready for testing soon after New Year

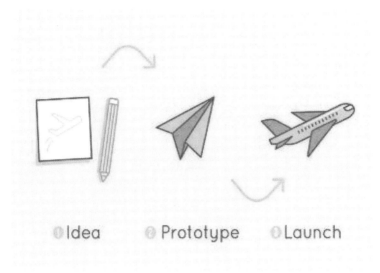

① Idea   ② Prototype   ③ Launch

When old Santa awoke from his post-Christmas nap —
around Easter — he heard an insistent tap-tap.
He threw open his door,
            and the drone that was knocking.
flew in, to deliver a filled Christmas stocking.

Santa welcomed technology — no luddite, he.
He went over Em's drawings with thinly-veiled glee.
His eyes were a-twinkle, his morning smile, gappy.
"Give 'em antlers, to keep the traditionalists happy"

A ut tempor
B pellentesque
C aliquam po

• minima veniam
  et harum quidem

• augue

B

• ut enim ad
  veniam

• et accusamus et
  dignissimos

A

C

• euismod

• augue

• vel eum iure
  et accusamus et

• et accusamus et

• dignissimos

"With a flight deck
controlling them all from the sleigh
"we could beta-test next week — perhaps Saturday."

But the older elves muttered

though younger ones
cheered

and some glitches occurred, as the doubters had feared.

Busy months hurried past until summer was gone.
Father Christmas pushed Emmie to move things along
till, at last, Santa's sleigh had its instrumentation.
The elves shuffled out for the grand demonstration.

One took off and crash-dived, and two flew away,
with another attacked by a large bird of prey.

A couple collided and one hit the wall,
and some couldn't pull up their stockings at all.

While, it's true, some delivered their load as directed,
still more work was needed before 'twas perfected.
All the younger, brash elven-folk
                    jeered and they laughed,
while the older ones claimed the whole idea was daft.

The concept was fantasy, science fiction, crass...
" 'Cos you can't replace reindeer, and Emmie's a lass."
Angry more with themselves for beginning to dream
of a cushier Christmas, with Emmie's bold scheme.

But Santa smiled kindly and smothered a chuckle.
"Twere worth trying, lass.'
Then he tightened his buckle
December was on them.
While Em tweaked her coding,
the others were sorting and packing, and loading.

The adverts and streetlights and windows of shops
were a-glitter with tinsel and other yule props

And younger elves tidied and swept and made tea

in keen
anticipation of
Christmas-to-be.

'Twas the night before Christmas,

                  when children in bed
had no inkling of Santa's sleigh parked overhead,

      as the elves filled the skies

                on their winged, metal steeds
with brass antlers to steer them at dizzying speeds

Old St. Nick and the reindeer could rest their tired feet

While the elf-guided drones made their drops in each street.

Then, trailing like stardust, they followed the sleigh

Wishing peace, health and laughter to all on their way.

About the Author

Cathy Cade is a retired librarian
who started creative writing
with annual reports and has continued
writing fiction in retirement.

Cathy has been published in *Scribble, Best of British, Tales of the Forest* and *Flash Fiction* magazine, *The Poet,* (Summer 2020) and *To Hull and Back Short Story Anthology (2018).*

Cathy can be found online at **cathy-cade.com**

If you enjoyed this book,
please leave a review on Amazon

More from Cathy

Euphemia Ffinch, godmother to Cindy-Ella, has been travelling since retiring as nanny to the Regalian royal family.

Buttons the dog lives in the basement with Cindy, whose stepmother – no dog lover – treats her as a servant.

Prince Alfred of Regalia dreads his birthday ball. His stutter gets worse in company, and the daughters of the nobility look down on him. (They are all taller than he is.) He'd rather invite the girl he met online.

Euphemia learns that Cindy's father has died. Her intuition tells her she is needed back in Regalia.

But Cindy hasn't read the fairy tales and has her own plans. Somebody has other plans for Euphemia too, and Buttons isn't sure he has a future to plan for.

Available on Amazon

Witch Way

and other ambiguous stories

Witch Way

and other ambiguous stories

Cathy Cade

Characters who aren't all they seem – or are they? You decide.

A tale inspired by the White Rabbit, one set in the shadow of Vesuvius, and one in a garden pond.

Meet Mirlings and Brownies, a misguided confidante, an unlikely Samaritan, a trainee mortician,

and a witch...

or not.

Available on Amazon

Barney

Barney chased a rabbit;

it hopped down a rabbit-hole:

A burrow in a grassy bank that called to Barney's soul.

Terriers love to dig, so Barney dug into the muck.

The burrow narrowed; Barney pushed and scrabbled.

He was stuck!

~ ~ ~

To read the rest of Barney's story (free), go to...
https://commaful.com/play/cathycade/barney/

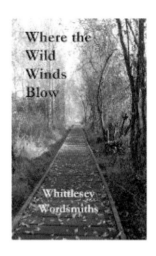

Cathy's stories and verse can also be found in the anthologies, *Where the Wild Winds Blow* and *A Following Wind* from the Whittlesey Wordsmiths.

These stories, poems and memoirs are the responses of a U3A creative writing group to our varying monthly challenges and celebrate the very different ways our imaginations interpret the same brief.

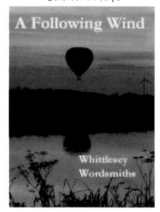

Find them on Amazon.

Printed in Poland
by Amazon Fulfillment
Poland Sp. z o.o., Wrocław

64843097R00016